My Super Swe
Recovery Cookbook

Published under licence by Brown Dog Books and
The Self-Publishing Partnership, 7 Green Park Station, Bath BA1 1JB

www.selfpublishingpartnership.co.uk

ISBN printed book: 978-1-78545-071-6

Cover design by Kevin Rylands
Book internals designed by Andrew Easton

My Super Sweet Recovery Cookbook

Recipes designed to help people with eating disorders in their journey of recovery

By Nicola Davis

Thank you

Writing this book would not have been possible without the many generous donations from my friends, family and supporters.

I would also like to thank my parents who encouraged my recovery from anorexia, and Martin who stuck by me while I was at my worst.

I must also thank the anorexia teams at both CAMHS and Cotswold House, my local doctor's surgery and Bath A&E. It was all of you who pushed me to make the worthwhile leap into recovery.

Finally, thank you to the Corsham School who supported me through my studies when I was too ill to attend school.

Contents

My Battle With Anorexia

I was diagnosed with anorexia when I was 16.

Looking back, there was not one specific reason, but a combination of many that had built up to this one moment. I was a competitive gymnast, training up to 15 hours a week. I had a history of depression and self-harm. I had recently moved schools. And my previous relationship had been difficult.

I began to lose weight, slowly, then all at once. I was affected by binge eating followed by bulimia, but my main battle was with anorexia nervosa. My head was not the same; my mind did not belong to me. Truthfully, it is hard to remember this phase of my life, as it was such a blur.

The next thing I knew, I was referred to my local anorexia services. I fought with them for months, arguing I was 'too fat' to be considered anorexic. Weigh-ins would become a regular part of my weekly routine, and I became deceitful, trying to hide my weight loss.

At age 18 I finished my A-levels; I believe this is was my turning point. I could say goodbye to some of the horrible memories that I associated with my school life. I chose to enter what seemed terrifying at the time, recovery! Leaving school I felt more like an adult, and wanted to take control of my own life. Rather than following strict meal plans, being monitored every time I ate, and weekly weigh-ins, I agreed with my medical team to start recovery, on my own terms! It may have been contrary to the standard medical advice but it worked for me. Food was a struggle but, day by day, I was able to eat more. I reached my 'restored' weight and my mind was becoming my own again.

Although I still do struggle on a daily basis, I now consider myself recovered. Anorexia is an illness that will stay with me for the rest of my life but I have learnt how to combat the triggers, thoughts and feelings associated with it.

Now, I want to pass on my story to help others.

Introduction

This book is aimed specifically at those struggling with eating disorders. It should act as a both a guide and a helping hand, providing you with easy, guilt-free recipes.

The recipes are split into three main sections: breakfast, lunch and dinner. However, there are also sections for snacks and desserts, vital parts of your meal plan.

If a recipe seems too hard right now you can try the 'Too Hard?' variation to help you build up your confidence. Once you become more comfortable with each recipe, you can look at the 'Experiment by' section, where you will find yummy additions to add to your meal, making it extra tasty.

I made the decision to be a vegetarian when I was a child, so naturally many of the recipes in this book are suitable for vegetarians. However, in many recipes I have included a non-vegetarian adaptation, which is usually described in the 'Experiment by' section.

Throughout the book you will also find general advice and tips on recovering from an eating disorder.

Please note, this book is based on my personal experience and is what worked for me. This should not be viewed as medical advice, more as a personal journey.

I wish you all the best with your recovery, and I hope this book can help you

Nicola

How To Use This Book

First and foremost, this book should act as a guide and reference for those in recovery from eating disorders. Each recipe is designed to ease you back into eating more comfortably rather than for gaining weight!

Portions

The portions shown are the recommended sizes you should be aiming for in recovery. However, I understand how some of these may seem too hard at this point. My best advice is to practise making each portion as recommended, eat as much as you can (these are normal-sized portions, I promise!) and store the rest as leftovers for another time.

Calories

I have purposely chosen to avoid displaying the calories of each meal, as you should be aiming to stop this behaviour. Counting calories can be very addictive, so it may be hard to begin with, and I'm sure you will try to look them up yourself! But my point is: obsessively counting calories is not 'normal' and in fact can often jeopardise your recovery.

'Too hard?' and 'Experiment by...'

Imagine each recipe as a stepping-stone towards recovery. The first step uses smaller portions and less-scary ingredients; this step can be seen in the 'Too hard?' section. The second step is the main recipe, this is what you should always be aiming for. The third step, 'Experiment by…' is the final step towards complete recovery: learning to experiment with foods and flavours to suit your personal preference rather than choosing whatever is 'healthiest'.

Symbols

V Vegetarian

Why Choose Recovery?

Choosing recovery will be the most rewarding, worthwhile and positive decision you ever make in your life... I promise!

The first, and the hardest, step to recovery is deciding *yourself* that you want to get better.

Once you have decided this, you are halfway there.

It can be difficult to motivate yourself on your low days, so make sure that you communicate how you are feeling with those close to you.

Recovering mentally

Alongside recovering physically, it is just as important to recover mentally. Make sure that you have someone to talk to, whether it be your family, friends, therapist or counsellor. There is a list of people you can talk to at the end of this book.

Many people with eating disorders also hear a voice inside their head, often identified as their eating disorder. Here is how to combat this voice:

- Identify this voice as your eating disorder. This is not the real you.
- Tell your eating disorder to STOP pestering you; you are in control, not it! Say this out loud if it helps.
- Whenever you hear this voice, acknowledge it and question what it is saying. Is this a normal thing for people to think? Does this make sense? Is there any knowledge or evidence to back this up? Most likely, the answer will be no. This is because your ED is a liar!
- Try to distract yourself from the thoughts. Talk to a friend, or do some reading.

Relapsing

Relapsing is a normal part of recovery... it will happen. It can happen in many different ways such as binge eating, over exercising, purging, or fasting. If you relapse, it is important to remind yourself that you are not a bad person for doing so. You can still recover, and all is not lost! Everyone has good and bad days so if you struggle one day, try to start afresh the next day and keep your mind on the end goal, not the ups and downs along the way. Skip to the centrefold of this book for my personal experience on relapsing.

20 distractions for when you feel low

- Have a bubble bath
- Do some drawing or colouring in
- Read a book
- Go for a short walk
- Watch your favourite movie
- Bake something yummy
- Make a friendship bracelet
- Go shopping
- Talk to a friend
- Play a game
- Paint your nails
- Have a nap
- Do some gentle yoga/meditation
- Tidy your room
- Listen to your favourite music
- Play with your pets
- Write a book/comic/diary
- Do some gardening
- Watch funny YouTube videos
- Watch your favourite TV series

Your Personal Recovery Meal Plan

Many people refer to a healthy diet as a balance between all the food groups. This can be very difficult to follow when recovering from an eating disorder. To start off with, follow this meal plan, using foods you are comfortable with:

Weeks 1-2

Aim to have breakfast, lunch and dinner every day. You may want someone to join you for moral support. If you are used to skipping breakfast, try it every other day. This may seem like a huge step right now, if it is too hard I understand! Just take it one day at a time, with your recovery in mind.

Weeks 3-4

Add in a snack once a day. This could be in between lunch and dinner, or maybe before bed. If this is too hard, add a snack into your meal plan every other day. Remember, snacks aren't always 'unhealthy'; they are a vital part in a healthy diet. They keep your blood sugar balanced in between meals and will really help you stay focused, whether it be at school, work or just at home!

Week 5

Feeling stronger, mentally and physically? Yay! Add another snack into your meal plan. This can be at any time in the day, but I suggest aiming to have a snack in between mealtimes or before bedtime. If a second snack is too hard, try to have a liquid snack, like my refreshing smoothies or a small glass of fruit juice.

Week 6

We don't want to go too hard too fast… This week, try to vary your meals slightly; it's easy to get stuck into a boring routine. You don't need to increase your intake if you don't feel up for this yet.

Week 7

You are seven weeks into recovery! High five! This week add a bed-time snack to your meal plan. I cannot express just how much having an evening snack helped me… It will help you sleep much better and wake up feeling ready to fight another day.

Week 8

From here onwards… you are in charge! Don't let this daunt you – some people find that meal plans really aid their recovery – so why not write your own? Experiment by slightly increasing your meal sizes bit by bit, but don't forget to snack! Try some new recipes and have a sip of juice or milk every morning with your breakfast

Breakfast

Breakfast is the most important meal of the day!
It will give you all the energy you need to wake up fully and function until lunchtime.
I recommend having a small glass of juice or milk with your chosen breakfast every morning. This may be too hard to start with (I had many breakfast-time tantrums!) so add it into your meal plan gradually, perhaps once a week to begin with.

Warm-Me-Up Porridge

Serves 1 (V)

Porridge is my all-time favourite breakfast. It can be altered completely to suit your preferences, and it isn't as boring as it may seem! Don't worry if it seems like a large portion before cooking… once the milk has been absorbed it will shrink to a 'normal' serving size.

Ingredients

30g porridge oats

200ml semi skimmed milk

Method

Put the oats and milk into a saucepan and bring to the boil. Turn down the heat and simmer for 4–5 minutes, stirring occasionally. Leave to cool for 2 minutes and serve in a cute bowl!

Too hard?

Use almond, coconut or rice milk instead of semi-skimmed milk. If this is still too hard begin by using water instead of milk, and over time, replace more and more of the water with milk.

Experiment by…

- adding ½ teaspoon of sugar or honey.
- adding a handful of fresh fruit such as chopped banana or blueberries! These always taste nice alongside a tablespoon of fresh yoghurt.
- adding a tablespoon of single or double cream for a creamier, smoother tasting porridge.
- sprinkling some of my homemade granola on top – see page 18.

Egg and Soldiers

Serves 1 (V)

Eggs contain all the yummy goodness of protein, vitamins, minerals and essential amino acids. Perfect for starting your day right.

Ingredients

1 egg, large or small, you choose
1 slice of bread
Butter

Method

Put the egg, gently and slowly, into a saucepan of boiling water, making sure all the egg is covered. Boil for 4-5 minutes, the larger the egg, the longer the boiling time.

While waiting, put your bread into the toaster. Once the egg is cooked place it in an egg-cup and gently cut off the top.

Butter your toast and cut into small strips. These taste great dunked in the yolk! Serve immediately.

Too hard?

Start with a simple boiled egg. When you feel comfortable, introduce the soldiers one by one; you are building an army!

Experiment by…

- trying different spreads on your toast, starting with low-fat spread, and building up to yummy things like peanut butter or chocolate spread.
- adding a pinch of pepper or salt on top of the egg for extra yummy flavour.
- trying different types of bread, maybe wholemeal, white or seeded bread (my favourite)!

Healthy Granola

Serves 5 (V)

Oats have been proven to lower your cholesterol and reduce your risk of heart failure or cardiovascular disease. This recipe is simply oats, seeds and berries – an 'au naturel' recipe for good health. This may seem like a lot of ingredients but remember that this makes 5 portions and will keep for weeks.

Ingredients

3 tsp vegetable oil
45ml golden syrup
3 tsp honey
3 drops vanilla extract
100g rolled oats
50g mixed seeds (such as pumpkin, sunflower, sesame)
30g flaked almonds
50g dried berries/raisins
15g coconut flakes or desiccated coconut

Method

Heat oven to 150ºC/fan 130ºC/gas 2.

Mix together the oil, golden syrup, honey and vanilla in a large bowl. Tip in all the remaining ingredients, except the dried fruit and coconut, and mix well. Tip the granola onto a greased baking sheet and spread evenly.

Bake for 10–15 minutes, then mix in the coconut and dried fruit, and bake for 5–10 minutes more. Remove from the oven and scrape onto a flat tray to cool.

Serve with cold milk or yogurt.

The granola can be stored in an airtight container for up to a month.

Too hard?

Serve smaller portions of granola and fill the gap with freshly chopped fruit such as banana or berries.

Experiment by…

- sprinkling 20g of chocolate drops into the granola once it has fully cooled down.
- using the granola as a healthy topping for snacks such as yoghurts or even milkshakes.

Poached Egg

Serves 1 (V)

I have already mentioned the various nutritional values of eggs, but this method is particularly healthy. No oil or butter is needed, unlike frying, meaning there is little fat in this recipe and it seems a bit less scary.

Ingredients

1 egg, large or small, you choose
1 slice of bread
Butter

Method

Half-fill a saucepan of water and bring to a simmer. Crack the egg into a cup and put to one side. Turn down the heat very slightly, and use the end of a spatula to create a whirlpool in the centre of the pan. Carefully pour the egg into the centre of the whirlpool and leave for 3 minutes.

Meanwhile, pop the bread into the toaster, and butter when done. Once the egg is cooked use the spatula to pick it up, dabbing off the excess water, and place on top of the toast.

Too hard?

Begin with the poached egg. Once comfortable, add half a slice of toast. Over time increase the amount of toast to one full slice. Trust me, the egg won't feel so lonely.

Experiment by...

- adding ketchup or a pinch of salt/pepper for extra flavour.
- serving with a slice or two of smoked salmon.
- chopping a few of chives into small pieces and sprinkling them on top for added flavour and colour.

Breakfast Muffins

Makes 12 (V)

Muffins can seem scary, but look closer at the ingredients of this recipe and you will see just healthy alternatives to the average recipe. Not only this, but the savoury feel of this muffin makes it great for breakfast without feeling too guilty. This recipe makes 12 muffins so freeze some for later or share them with your family.

Ingredients

1 egg
200ml semi-skimmed milk
80ml vegetable oil
A few drops of vanilla extract
180g plain wholemeal flour
80g rolled oats
100g soft brown sugar
10g baking powder
10g bicarbonate of soda
½ tsp salt
2 mashed bananas
60g raisins

Method

Preheat the oven to 200°C/fan 180°C/gas 6 and line a 12-hole muffin tin with muffin cases.

Mix together the egg, milk, oil and vanilla extract in a large bowl and add the mashed bananas.

In a separate bowl mix all of the dry ingredients together. Fold the dry ingredients into the bowl with the wet ingredients and mix. Spoon the mixture evenly into the muffin cases.

Bake for 15 minutes then leave on a wire rack to cool.

Store in an air-tight container or freeze for later.

Too hard?

Use 18 cupcake cases instead to make smaller, mini muffins! Check them after 10–12 minutes,
as smaller ones will cook more quickly.

Experiment by…

- replacing the raisins with other dried fruits, or yummy chocolate drops!
- serving with a dollop of double cream, lightly buttered, or with some fresh fruit on the side.
- having one as a snack, between meals or before bed.

Green Tea and Berry Smoothie

Serves 1 (V)

If you prepare the tea beforehand and leave it in the fridge, this can make a great on-the-go breakfast for when you are in a rush! And do I need to explain the benefits of green tea!? I could go on for hours....

Ingredients

150ml water
2 green tea bags
50g yoghurt (I like vanilla)
40g blackberries
40g raspberries
1 banana
3 ice cubes

Method

Boil the water and diffuse the tea bags in a mug for 5 minutes.

Remove the tea bags and leave to cool completely.

Add all of the ingredients, including the tea and ice cubes, to a blender and blend for 3 minutes until smooth.

Too hard?

Lower the amount of yoghurt used and replace with more banana or berries.

Try low-fat frozen yoghurt.

Experiment by...

- using different fruits such as strawberries or blueberries.
- adding 10g almonds for extra protein.
- going green, replacing the berries with spinach, white grapes and a teaspoon of honey.

Banana Oat Milkshake

Serves 1 (V)

Oats can seem a bit scary or even 'pointless' in a smoothie, but I promise they are not. The blended oats will add body to the smoothie whilst being the main source of energy to power you up for the day.

Ingredients

1 banana
150ml semi-skimmed milk
1 large pinch cinnamon
2 tsps honey
3 dessert spoons porridge oats
3 ice cubes

Method

Add all of the ingredients to the blender and blend for 3 minutes until smooth.

Too hard?

Replace the semi-skimmed milk with almond, coconut or rice milk.

Lower the amount of oats used.

Experiment by…

- adding various fruits, such as a handful of strawberries or blueberries.
- adding 10g almonds.

Lunch

Lunch is often a rushed meal, eaten at the desk, eaten on the move, or even avoided. Make sure to allocate a full hour in your day to sit down and eat your lunch properly, perhaps in the park, with a good book or a friend!

Quinoa Salad

Serves 1 (V)

This salad may take a little longer than others to make, but it is worth it! The quinoa makes this recipe perfect for vegetarians or vegans, acting as a high source of protein. It can be made the day before and kept in the fridge, ready to grab at lunchtime.

Ingredients

40g quinoa
200ml water
½ sweet potato, peeled and chopped into small cubes
25g mixed salad leaves
50g mixed beans (such as chickpeas, kidney beans..)
10g Feta cheese
salt and pepper for seasoning

Method

Pre heat the oven to 200°C/fan 180°C/gas 6.

Rinse the quinoa thoroughly and add to a pan with the water. Bring to the boil, cover and reduce to a simmer for 15 minutes, stirring occasionally until all the water has been absorbed. Leave to cool in the fridge.

Place the chopped sweet potato onto a baking tray and add a dash of olive oil, seasoning with salt and pepper. Roast in the oven for 15 minutes. Leave to cool.

Rinse the salad leaves and add to a serving bowl with the beans and cheese. Add the quinoa and sweet potatoes and mix well.

Too hard?

Leave half of the ready-made quinoa in the fridge to eat another time and replace with more salad leaves.

Experiment by…

- adding salad dressing, page 65.
- having a slice of French stick, bread or a few crackers on the side.

New Potato Salad

Serves 1 (V)

Potatoes can seem very scary, but they are much healthier than you think. They contain potassium, which lowers blood pressure, and multiple vitamins, fibre and iron!

Ingredients

150g new potatoes, washed and cut in half
50g asparagus
A few parsley leaves, finely chopped
2 radishes, thinly sliced
10g spinach
10g walnuts, chopped
15g olives, cut in half
10g goat's cheese

Method

Fill a pan with water and bring to the boil, add the potatoes and cook for 10 minutes. Add the asparagus to the pan and boil for a further 5-7 minutes.

Drain the potatoes and asparagus, then mix in a bowl with the parsley leaves and creamy salad dressing on page 65. (Image shown replaces the Dijon mustard with wholegrain mustard).

Toss in a bowl with the other ingredients and serve.

Too hard?

Use fewer potatoes and replace with a handful of mixed salad leaves. Begin without any dressing or serve it on the side as a dip.

Experiment by...

- frying 30g mushrooms in a little olive oil and mixing them into the salad.
- trying different salad dressings, page 65.
- adding 1 rasher of chopped cooked bacon.

Vegetable Soup

Serves 2-3 (V)

There shouldn't be anything to be scared of here; this soup is just pure vegetables! You can easily replace the vegetables in this example with any others you may prefer, or even make a vegetable and bacon soup by reading the 'experiment by…' section.

Ingredients

½ onion, chopped
1 stick celery, chopped
1 leek, chopped
2 tbsp olive oil
½ clove garlic, crushed
3 large carrots, peeled and chopped
300g potatoes, peeled and chopped
500ml vegetable stock
salt and pepper for seasoning

Method

In a large saucepan, fry the onion, celery and leek with the oil until soft and translucent. Add the garlic and fry for 1 minute, then add the rest of the vegetables and sauté for 5 minutes.

Add the vegetable stock, then cover and simmer for 20–30 minutes, stirring occasionally. Add salt and pepper to taste.

When the vegetables are fully cooked, blend in a food processor or blender until smooth, then serve.

Too hard?

Replace the potatoes with sweet potato or other vegetables you may feel more comfortable with.

Use 700ml vegetable stock, which will make more portions but each portion will be thinner in consistency.

Experiment by…

- serving with a slice of bread or French stick.
- adding extra goodness such as sweetcorn, croutons, chickpeas etc.
- topping with a dollop of crème fraîche, crumbled feta cheese or fried crispy bacon pieces.

Chicken Caesar Salad

Serves 1

Caesar salads are mostly known for their dressing, but don't let this put you off. Use my low-fat Caesar dressing on page 65, which replaces heavy cream with low-fat yoghurt.

Ingredients

1 tbsp olive oil, plus extra for coating the chicken
1 slice brown bread or a slice of French stick
45g Romaine or Cos lettuce
1 skinless, boneless chicken breast
15g Parmesan cheese
salt

Method

Warm the oil in a small frying pan and slice the bread into small cubes. Toss the bread and a pinch of salt in the pan until well toasted on every side. Leave to cool, then mix in a bowl with the lettuce.

Brush the chicken breast with a little oil and fry in a pre-heated pan over a medium heat. Cook for around 5-7 minutes on each side then remove from the heat, making sure the chicken is cooked all the way through.

Cut into bite-size strips and add to the salad, grating Parmesan on top. Serve with Caesar dressing on page 65.

Too hard?

Try the salad without croutons first, or replace the chicken with a handful of pre-cooked tofu or Quorn pieces.

Serve the dressing on the side and use as a dip.

Experiment by...

- adding 2 rashers cooked bacon.
- trying the salad with different dressings shown on page 65.

Parma Ham Salad

Serves 1

Parma ham is full of flavour, so a small amount goes a long way. For vegetarians, replace the ham with 1 hard-boiled egg, sliced into chunks, and 15g fresh spinach.

Ingredients

20g mixed salad leaves
15g toasted walnuts, chopped
30g cooked beetroot, chopped
3 slices Parma ham/prosciutto
20g mozzarella

Method

Mix the salad leaves, walnuts and beetroot in a bowl. Tear the ham and mozzarella into smaller pieces and add to the salad.

Best served with balsamic salad dressing on page 65.

Too hard?

Replace the mozzarella with 10g grated Parmesan. Try not to avoid cheese completely but rather lessen the amount and grate it thinly so it is less 'in your face' and more evenly distributed.

Experiment by…

- trying with different dressings shown on page 65.
- serving with a slice of French stick.

Avocado Salad Wrap

Serves 1 (V)

Wraps are often filled with various thick sauces, which may put you off, but this recipe should tease you back with no sauce whatsoever, using mashed avocado to keep the wrap lush and moist.

Ingredients

1 ripe avocado, peeled and thinly sliced
1 tortilla/wrap of your choice
20g lettuce
1 medium tomato, thinly sliced
15g grated Parmesan or Cheddar cheese
Pinch of salt and pepper

Method

In a small bowl, mash half of the avocado with a fork and spread over the tortilla. Layer the centre of the wrap with chopped lettuce, tomato and the remaining avocado. Sprinkle with cheese and salt and pepper.

Fold in two opposite edges of the tortilla about 2 inches, then roll the tortilla from an unfolded side into a 'log' shape. Slice in half and serve.

Too hard?

Begin with only 1 half of the wrap served with a side salad or fresh fruits. Store the other half in the fridge for later.

Experiment by…

- replacing the avocado spread with a tablespoon of hummus or mayonnaise.
- adding a little extra cheese, then grilling on a medium heat for 5 minutes.
- replacing the avocado with 1 cooked chicken breast, sliced thinly.

Pasta Salad

Serves 1 (V)

This pasta salad is made a little less scary by being combined with lots of fresh salad leaves. It can also be prepared beforehand and stored in the fridge, so you can eat it whenever you feel like it.

Ingredients

65g dry pasta
½ avocado, peeled
15g mixed salad leaves
30g mozzarella
10g spinach
40g cherry tomatoes, halved
10g pine nuts
olive oil
salt and pepper for seasoning

Method

Put the pasta in a pan of boiling water with a large pinch of salt. Boil for 10–12 minutes, stirring occasionally. Once cooked, drain the pasta, hold under running cold water for a few minutes, and leave to cool completely.

Meanwhile, chop the avocado, spinach and salad leaves to your preferred size and prepare the mozzarella, using a melon baller to cut it into similar-sized balls.

Put all of the ingredients into a bowl and mix. Drizzle a little olive oil and a pinch of pepper on top for dressing.

Too hard?

Reduce the amount of pasta used and replace with more salad.

Leave out the cheese.

Experiment by…

- adding some croutons or cooked vegetables such as asparagus.
- adding a tablespoon of pesto and mixing well.
- adding some chopped, crispy bacon, ham or cooked chicken.

Vegetable Omelette

Serves 1 (V)

Omelettes were always my 'safe food' because, to put it simply, all that's in them is egg and vegetables! These are also great for the fussy eater because you can mix up this simple recipe however you like, adding as little or as much as you want.

Ingredients

50g courgettes, chopped
50g mushrooms, washed and chopped
30g mangetout or green beans
2 eggs
1 large knob of butter
45g cherry tomatoes, cut in half
20g fresh spinach
salt and pepper for seasoning

Method

Fry the courgettes in a frying pan with a knob of butter for two minutes, then add the mushrooms and cook until slightly browned. Boil the mangetout in another pan for five minutes, then drain and put to one side with the other vegetables.

Crack the eggs into a small bowl and whisk with the salt and pepper.

Heat a knob of butter in a separate large frying pan and pour in the egg evenly over the pan. Use a spatula to lift the edges of the omelette and let the uncooked mixture run underneath.

When the top is nearly set, sprinkle the cooked vegetables, tomatoes and spinach over half of the omelette, cook for a few more minutes then turn off the heat.

Use the spatula to flip one half of the omelette over the other and serve immediately.

Too hard?

Try a plain omelette without vegetables, or use just 1 egg to begin with. Note: this is much better than only using the egg whites, as the yolks are the parts which are packed with vitamins, folic acid and Omega-3.

Experiment by…

- grating 15g cheese either into the uncooked mixture first or on top of the cooked omelette.
- adding 20g of diced ham or cooked bacon into the uncooked mixture.
- serving with a side salad or French stick.

Half Way

Half way through writing this book I suffered a relapse.

This is the first many will know about it. I kept it a secret, listening to the voices in my head which told me I was a 'fat pig' and that I never should have started recovery in the first place.

I know exactly why I relapsed. I felt too 'fake' to be writing a recovery book.
People would look at me and think:
'She's too fat to have suffered from anorexia… she must be lying!'

I honestly pictured myself holding this book in my hands, and people looking at me, disgusted at what 'recovery' and weight restoration looks like. *'No way am I going to start recovery if I will end up that fat!'*

And was I fat? Am I fat? No! Honestly, I am thinner than the average girl my age, even at a truly healthy weight.

Why am I telling you this?

Because it's real. I want you to know that I still struggle, even now. I want you to believe me when I say that 'recovery is possible', but I *need* you to know that recovery is not the perfect image it is bigged up to be. It is not easy, and it is not a straight road ahead.

Real recovery is fighting every single day: to eat that last spoonful, to walk your dog without counting each step, to be able to look at yourself in the mirror without crying, to *want* to live your life to the fullest.

So please, if you are struggling, I understand. But please don't give up. Turn the page, move on. Each day, each minute, and each second is a fresh start.

Dinner

Dinner is often a sociable time, where families eat together.
Try to ditch your bedroom and join the family to talk about your day and get things off your chest. Eating with others can be really hard, so don't forget to be open about how you are feeling.

Vegetable Risotto

Serves 1 (V)

Risotto is one of my all-time favourites for dinner. When starting my recovery, I would have this every evening with as many different vegetables as I could get my hands on! I suggest experimenting with brightly coloured veg to add colour to your meal.

Ingredients

300ml water
1 stock cube (chicken or vegetable)
45g chopped courgettes
60g chopped mushrooms
40g Arborio rice
45g peas
30g green beans
60g chopped broccoli
30g spinach
1 large knob of butter
parsley or other fresh herbs

Method

Boil the water and put it in a jug with the stock cube. Mix and leave to the side.

Fry the courgettes in a saucepan with a large knob of butter and add the mushroom after 2 minutes. When they are almost cooked, stir in the rice.

Add a little of the stock at a time and stir often for 10–15 minutes, while the rice absorbs the stock. Add the rest of the vegetables and cook until all the stock has been absorbed and the rice is soft.

Leave to cool for a few minutes and serve, with a sprinkle of parsley for decoration.

Too hard?

Lower the ratio of rice to vegetables to what you can manage.

Over time, increase the proportion of rice.

Experiment by:

- adding some grated Parmesan or crumbled feta cheese on top for some extra flavour.
- serving with a slice of bread or French stick.
- adding 50g chopped cooked beetroot at the end – my favourite addition and it turns the whole dish purple!

Sweet Potato Mash

Serves 1 (V)

Sweet potato is often seen as the 'healthier version' of the common potato and it adds a lovely colour to the dish, so I couldn't resist introducing you to this recipe! Over time, when you become more comfortable with the recipe, try it with common potatoes, which you may even prefer.

Ingredients

1 large sweet potato, peeled and diced
15g butter
20ml semi-skimmed milk
60g mixed vegetables
salt and pepper for seasoning

Method

Fill a saucepan with water and bring to the boil. Add a large pinch of salt, then add the sweet potato and boil for 10–15 minutes until tender.

Meanwhile, in a separate saucepan boil the vegetables for 10 minutes and drain.

Once the potato is completely tender, drain off the water. Add the butter and milk, then mash with a potato masher.

Season with pepper, stir in the vegetables, and serve.

Too hard?

Use a smaller-sized sweet potato and replace with more vegetables. Replace the semi-skimmed milk with almond, rice or coconut milk and reduce the amount of butter used.

Experiment by…

- trying the recipe with common potatoes instead, or do half and half.
- adding gravy for extra flavour.
- chopping up one or two sausages and serving on the side.

Stuffed Mushroom 'Burger'

Serves 1

I always avoided burgers when I was ill, and when confronted with one I would make any excuse possible! But this recipe replaces the 'scary' bread with healthy mushroom, and rather than using processed meat which you may be wary of, you can stack up your own 'burger' using whatever you like!

Ingredients

1 large Portobello mushroom
2 slices aubergine
½ clove garlic, crushed
½ slice brown bread, blitzed into crumbs
1 egg yolk
1 large pinch chopped chives
1 tbsp vegetable oil
1-2 rashers of bacon, cut into small even chunks
30g baby leaf spinach
20g iceberg lettuce
salt and pepper for seasoning

Method

Pre-heat the oven to 200°C/fan 180°C/gas 6.

Remove the stalk from the mushroom and place skin-side down, on a small baking tray alongside the aubergine slices.

Melt a knob of butter in a frying pan and add the garlic and breadcrumbs. Cook for two minutes until lightly toasted. Cool, then add the egg yolk, salt, pepper and chives and mix. Spoon into the mushroom. Drizzle the mushroom and aubergine with a little olive oil, then bake for 5–7 minutes until golden.

Meanwhile, fry the bacon in a pan with the oil until cooked, and boil the spinach in a pan of water for 1–2 minutes, then drain.

Stack up your 'burger', beginning with the mushroom and topping with bacon. Best served with a side salad or fries.

Too hard?

Remove the bacon from the recipe and start without stuffing the mushroom.

Experiment by…

- sprinkling 20g feta cheese or 15g Parmesan on top.
- serving with a side salad, fries or my sweet potato crisps, see page 74.

Cute Mini Pizza

Makes 1 (V)

For me, pizza was always a no-no. But I will never forget the first time I tried it in my recovery, it was such a dream! This pizza has a super thin crust and if you are still unsure, follow my instructions to go cheese-less!

Ingredients

1 wholemeal pitta bread/sandwich thin
1 tbsp tomato sauce
10g grated Parmesan
1 mushroom, washed and chopped
10g baby leaf spinach
10g red pepper
fresh basil leaves

Method

Preheat the oven to 200°C/fan 180°C/gas 6.

Spread the tomato sauce evenly over the bread base and sprinkle the cheese on top. Add the toppings and place in the oven for 5–10 minutes.

Best served with a side salad.

Too hard?

Go cheese-less! This was actually the way traditional pizza was made hundreds of years ago. Reduce the cooking time to 4–6 minutes and, once cooked, add a little drizzle of vegetable oil for added moisture.

Experiment by…

- using different toppings such as chopped ham, cooked chorizo or bacon (as shown in the photo), or other vegetables.
- drizzling some olive oil on top.
- adding a dressing to your side salad, see page 65.

Stir Fry with Noodles

Serves 2

Not only is stir fry super-quick to cook, but it is filled with nutrients from the vegetables and protein from the meat. As always, this is a really versatile recipe and ingredients can be easily swapped or substituted!

Ingredients

1 pack/serving egg noodles (60g)
2 tbsp vegetable oil
60g Quorn 'chicken' pieces/1 small chicken breast, chopped into thin strips
1 cm piece fresh ginger, peeled and finely chopped
1 carrot, peeled and finely chopped
4 spears baby corn, sliced in half lengthways
½ red pepper, chopped
80g mushrooms, chopped
4 spears long stem broccoli, chopped
2 tsp soy sauce
salt and pepper for seasoning

Method

Put the noodles in a pan of boiling water and cook following the packet instructions. Drain, run under cold water, and put to one side.

Heat the oil on a high heat in a large frying pan/wok and cook the chicken/Quorn for 2–3 minutes. Add the ginger, carrot and baby corn and cook for a further 2 minutes. Add the rest of the vegetables and cook again for 2 minutes.

Add the noodles, salt and pepper, soy sauce then mix well and serve immediately.

Too hard?

Leave out the noodles and serve larger portions of the vegetables. This is actually a really common variation of stir fry!

Leave out the chicken or Quorn and introduce gradually as you get more confident.

Experiment by....

- replacing the noodles with cooked rice.
- trying different vegetables such as water chestnuts/ bamboo shoots, peas, green beans...

Sauces

It can be hard even to think about eating a sauce in the early stages of recovery, but they are a normal part of most meals. If any of these seem too hard at the moment, serve them in a separate bowl and use them as a 'dip'.

White Sauce – Serves 1 (V)

15g butter
15g flour
100ml milk
10g cheese
pinch of salt and pepper

Method

Melt the butter in a small saucepan and add the flour, mixing all the time to create a smooth paste. On a low heat add the milk, bit by bit, constantly stirring so it is a smooth consistency.

Once all the milk is added, grate the cheese and add to the pan. Increase the heat to a simmer and stir constantly until the sauce reaches your preferred consistency. Season to taste with salt and pepper.

Serve immediately.

Simple Bolognese Sauce – Serves 2–4

2 tbsp olive oil
1 small onion, finely chopped
60g sliced mushrooms
1 carrot (peeled and finely chopped)
1 garlic clove, crushed (optional)
100g lean minced beef or 100g Quorn mince
250g passata or ½ tin chopped tomatoes
1 pinch of dried mixed herbs
large pinch salt and pepper

Method

Heat the oil in a large saucepan and brown the onion slightly. Add the mushrooms, carrot and garlic, if using, then fry for 5 minutes.

Add the mince and cook for a further 5–10 minutes then drain off any excess oil. (Quorn mince will cook much quicker and won't need draining).

Stir in the passata, herbs and salt and pepper. Cover and simmer for 10–15 minutes.

Serve immediately. Any leftovers can be frozen for later.

Dressings

Similar to the sauces: if you are struggling, then serve the dressing in a separate bowl and use it as a dip. This is an easy way of easing you back into dressings without covering your whole salad with them.

Balsamic Salad Dressing – Serves 1–2

1 tbsp olive oil
2 tsp balsamic vinegar
1 tsp honey (optional)
pinch of salt and pepper

Creamy Salad Dressing – Serves 1–2

1 tbsp olive oil
2 tsp white wine vinegar
1 tsp Dijon mustard
1 tsp honey
pinch of salt and pepper

Healthy Caesar Dressing – Serves 1–2

1 ½ tbsps low fat Greek style yoghurt
1 tbsp lemon juice
1 tbsp olive oil
1 tsp Worcestershire sauce
½ garlic clove, crushed
salt and pepper

Method

Mix all of the ingredients together well, and drizzle over salad.

Snacks

Snacks are particularly important to keep your blood sugar levels up, but they can be really hard to introduce back into your day, as they may seem unnecessary and hard to justify. Try to have a snack in between each meal to keep you going, and also before bedtime to give you a great night's sleep!

P.S Each one of these snacks can also double up as a super-healthy dessert!

Strawberry and Banana Milkshake

Makes 1 (V)

I will never tire of milkshakes! The simplicity of them means you can mix up any combination and succeed, along with the added benefits of being filled with calcium and plenty of vitamins and minerals.

Ingredients

1 banana
5 strawberries
150ml semi-skimmed milk
3 ice cubes
few drops vanilla extract

Method

Chop the fruit into small chunks. Add all of the ingredients to a blender and blend for 2–3 minutes until smooth.

Too hard?

Use almond, coconut or rice milk instead of semi-skimmed. If this is still too hard use less milk and replace with a dash of water.

Experiment by…

- using different fruits such as berries (frozen berries are great as they stay fresh for weeks and they make the milkshake extra cold!).
- adding a teaspoon of honey before blending.
- adding a scoop of frozen yoghurt or vanilla ice cream before blending.

Simple Smoothies

Makes 1 (V)

Smoothies are great snacks for when you are on the move and, as with the milkshakes, they can be completely re-invented with ease. Follow the same instructions for each smoothie, simply altering the ingredients.

Berry Smoothie

1 banana
80g mixed berries (strawberries/raspberries/blackberries)
150ml orange juice

Mango and Passion Fruit

½ mango
juice of 2 passion fruits
1 banana
150ml apple juice

Method

Peel and chop the fruit into small chunks. Add all of the ingredients to a blender and blend for 3 minutes until smooth. Pour over ice to serve.

Too hard?

Add a dash of water and reduce the amount of juice slightly.

Experiment by…

- using different fruits such as apple, pineapple, peach etc…
- adding 2tbsp natural yoghurt for an extra thick smoothie.

Blueberry Muffins

Makes 12 (V)

These muffins are really light and not too sweet to scare you off! Being full of fruit also helps them feel healthier. They taste great just out of the oven or can be stored for a handy on-the-go snack! Due to the high fruit content the muffins only keep fresh for 3-4 days, so I suggest freezing half for next week.

Ingredients

250g self-raising flour
1½ tsp baking powder
50g low fat margarine
75g granulated sugar
100g blueberries
2 eggs
235ml semi-skimmed milk
juice of half a lemon

Method

Preheat the oven to 180°C/fan 160°C/gas 4. Line a 12-hole muffin tin with muffin cases.

Sieve the flour and baking powder into a large bowl and add the margarine, rubbing gently until it resembles breadcrumbs. Add the sugar and blueberries.

Whisk the eggs, milk and lemon juice with a hand whisk and add to the bowl. Stir gently until the mixture is mixed in evenly.

Spoon the mixture into 12 muffin cases and bake for 20–25 minutes.

Too hard?

Use 18 cupcake cases instead to make smaller, mini muffins! Check them after 10–12 minutes, as smaller ones will cook more quickly.

Experiment by…

- sprinkling a bit of icing sugar on top of the muffins after cooking.
- adding a drizzle of warm custard for a yummy dessert.
- replacing the blueberries with blackcurrants, blackberries or dried fruit.

Sweet Potato Crisps

Serves 2 (V)

There is no reason for guilt with these crisps; by baking them rather than frying, the fat content is much lower, and you can add as much or as little salt as you like. Plus there are no additives or preservatives, and they really are easy to make!

Ingredients

1 sweet potato
2 tsp olive oil
2 tsp Soy sauce (optional)
Salt

Method

Set the oven to 180°C/fan 160°C/gas 4.

Scrub the sweet potato clean and using a mandolin or a knife, carefully cut the potato into even, thin slices. The thinner the slice, the crispier they will be.

Brush the potato slices on both sides with a little oil and soy sauce, if using. Lay the slices out on a baking tray and sprinkle a bit of salt on top.

Bake for 20–30 minutes until crisp, turning them over halfway through.

Leave to cool on a wire rack. They should be completely crispy when ready to eat.

Too hard?

Replace the sweet potato with apple and follow the same method, using just a sprinkle of ground cinnamon to flavour.

Experiment by…

- using different flavourings on top such as black pepper, nutmeg and paprika.
- adding a dip such as hummus.

Fruit Salad

Serves 2–4 (V)

Fruit salad is quite simply pure fruit, and can be eaten at any time of the day as a healthy fresh snack or a pudding; it is even great for breakfast! This is a super-healthy version as it uses lemon juice rather than sweetened syrup or orange juice.

Ingredients

1 apple
1 pear
1 kiwi
1 mango
1 handful of red and green grapes
5 strawberries
1 banana (optional)
2 tbsp lemon juice

Method

Peel and chop the apple, pear, kiwi and mango into similar sized chunks and put in a bowl. Add the other fruits and mix them up, pouring the lemon juice over the top. Serve immediately if using bananas.

Too hard?

Leave out the juice and start off with a simple bowl of fresh fruit.

Experiment by...

- adding 1 tablespoon of honey for extra sweetness.
- trying a variety of different fruits such as raspberries, melon or pineapple.
- serving with a tablespoon of natural yoghurt.

Blackberry Flapjack

Makes 12 (V)

The blackberries and apples in this flapjack will help you reach your 5 a day, plus it is a great and easy snack to wrap up and take out with you! The addition of the fruit makes it seem far less scary too, although it will only keep for 3–4 days, so I suggest freezing half for another time!

Ingredients

120g butter
80g Demerara sugar
2 tbsp golden syrup
250g rolled oats
1 large cooking apple, peeled and grated
250g blackberries, washed

Method

Preheat the oven to 180°C/fan 160°C/gas 4. Grease a 20-cm square cake tin and line with baking parchment.

Melt the butter, sugar and golden syrup in a saucepan over a medium heat.

When melted, remove from the heat and put in a bowl with the oats and grated apple. Gently stir in all the blackberries. Press the flapjack evenly into the tin.

Bake for 25–30 minutes until nicely browned and leave to cool in the tin on a wire rack before slicing into portions of your chosen size.

Too hard?

Substitute the golden syrup with the same amount of honey.

Cut into smaller pieces when serving.

Experiment by…

- trying different flavourings such as replacing the blackberries with other fruits or scrummy chocolate drops.

Healthy Desserts

Each one of these desserts can also double up as a super healthy snack for during the day or my favourite… before bedtime! Remember, you don't need an excuse to have dessert, ever! It is a vital part of recovery.

Apple Cake

(V)

This was my breakthrough recipe, the one that started this whole book off! Although some of the ingredients may seem scary at first, the main ingredient is just apples. Also, once it has come out of the oven you won't be able to resist the smell!

Ingredients

150g unsalted butter
150g soft dark brown sugar
150g golden syrup
200ml semi-skimmed milk
250g plain flour
1 tsp ground ginger
1 tsp ground cinnamon
1 ½ tsp baking powder
2 eggs
2 large apples, peeled and cut into large chunks

Method

Set the oven to 180°C /fan 160°C/gas 4. Grease and line a loaf tin.

Melt the butter, sugar and syrup in a pan. Add the milk and leave to cool.

Sift the flour, spices and baking powder into a large bowl. Add the cooled milk mixture and mix well. Fold in the eggs and apple and pour the mixture into the prepared tin.

Cook for 50–55 minutes and leave to cool before removing it from the tin.

Too hard?

Replace the golden syrup with natural honey and use almond, soy or coconut milk instead of semi-skimmed milk.

Experiment by…

- warming up a slice of the cake and adding a dash of custard or single cream on top.

Guilt-Free Hot Chocolate

Serves 1 (V)

Hot chocolate is my favourite bed-time snack, not only because it tastes so good but because the warm milk helps you sleep! This recipe stays clear of all the sugars and additives used in instant hot chocolate packets.

Ingredients

250ml semi-skimmed milk + 1 tbsp extra
2 rounded tsp unsweetened cocoa powder
1 tsp brown sugar (or sweetener of choice)
¼ tsp vanilla extract

Method

Place the milk in a small pan over a medium heat.

Place the cocoa powder, sugar and the extra tablespoon of milk in a small bowl. Whisk until a paste/thick mixture forms and the powder is absorbed.

Whisk the cocoa mixture into the milk and heat until you get to your required drinking temperature.

Too hard?

Use almond, coconut or rice milk instead of semi-skimmed milk.

Lower the quantity of milk and dilute with water.

Experiment by…

- sprinkling cinnamon or grated chocolate on top of the finished drink.
- adding a little whipped cream.
- serving with a biscuit to dip in!

Banana Bread

(V)

This is a really homely recipe to enjoy and tastes best served warm. You can slice it as thinly as you feel comfortable with, and reassure yourself that this is packed with vitamins and protein from the healthy bananas. Due to the high fruit content it only stays fresh for 3-4 days so why not freeze some for later.

Ingredients

150g caster sugar
50g softened butter
2 eggs
4 tbsps water
3 mashed bananas
150g plain wholemeal flour
1 tsp bicarbonate of soda
1 tsp baking powder

Method

Preheat the oven to 180°C/fan 160°/gas 4 and line a loaf tin with baking parchment.

Beat the sugar and butter in a bowl until smooth and creamy then add the eggs, water and bananas and mix until well blended. Fold in the flour, bicarbonate of soda and baking powder.

Spoon the mixture into the tin and bake for 40–45 minutes. Leave to cool in the tin on a wire rack, then serve.

Too hard?

Begin with small portions until you feel more comfortable.

Experiment by…

- sprinkling 25g chopped pecans or walnuts on top of the mixture before baking.
- adding 25g chocolate chips into the mixture before baking.

Berry Mousse

Makes 2 (V)

This recipe takes just 5 minutes to make and you're done! It is a really light and refreshing dessert, perfect for a hot summer's evening. It's mostly fresh fruit, with none of the cream or custard normally found in mousses. Best served straight away while the berries are still ice-cold, or stored in the fridge.

Ingredients

250g low-fat cream cheese
a few drops of lemon juice
25g icing sugar
125g mixed frozen berries (raspberries, blueberries…)

Method

Put the cream cheese and lemon juice into a bowl and sift in the icing sugar. Mix until smooth and creamy. Add the berries and mix gently until the mixture is streaked pink.

Best served instantly or kept refrigerated.

Too hard?

Leave the berries separate from the mixture and serve in two separate dishes. Dip the berries in as much mousse as is comfortable.

Replace the icing sugar with granulated sweetener.

Experiment by…

- breaking up 2 digestive biscuits and either sprinkling on top of each mousse or layer underneath, like a guilt free cheesecake!

Rice Pudding

Serves 4–6 (V)

My mum would always say 'why are you so scared, it's just rice!' and honestly, I don't know what I was ever scared of! Sometimes you just have to taste it to understand, and when I tasted my first rice pudding I fell in love.

Ingredients

100g pudding rice
50g caster sugar
700ml semi-skimmed milk
1 pinch grated nutmeg
1 bay leaf (optional)
1 knob of butter

Method

Heat oven to 150°C/fan 130°C/gas 2. Butter an 850ml heatproof baking dish.

Wash the rice and drain well and place in the dish with the sugar and milk. Mix gently, then sprinkle the nutmeg over and top with the bay leaf, if using.

Cook for 60-90 minutes, or until the pudding wobbles slightly when shaken. When cooked, dispose of the skin and spoon the pudding into individual serving bowls.

Best served warm.

Too hard?

Use almond, coconut or soya milk to replace the semi-skimmed milk.

Have a bowl of fresh fruit and add a spoonful of the rice pudding as a topping/dip instead.

Experiment by…

- serving alongside fresh fruit.
- using different flavourings in the pudding such as replacing the nutmeg with a teaspoon of vanilla extract.
- keeping the skin on top when serving (some people love it!)

Mini Blueberry Pancakes

Serves 3–4 (V)

These pancakes are really simple to make, and can be filled with as many fruits or berries as you like. They are also great served alongside fresh fruit and are guilt-free due to the high fruit content.

Ingredients

65g plain flour
½ tsp baking powder
¼ tsp salt
1 tbsp caster sugar
65ml milk
1 small egg
1 tbsp olive oil
50g blueberries
butter for frying

Method

Sift the flour, baking powder, salt and caster sugar into a large bowl. In a separate bowl, whisk together the milk, egg and oil. Beat the wet and dry mixtures together until you have a smooth batter then add the blueberries and mix gently.

Melt a knob of butter in a frying pan over a medium heat and add a ladle of batter. Once the bottom of the pancake becomes golden brown, flip it and cook on the other side. The pancake should rise to about 1cm thick. Repeat until all the batter is used up, and serve.

Too hard?

Add 50g extra berries or raisins. This will make more pancakes but each one will have less batter and more fruit.

Experiment by…

- drizzling some strawberry purée, golden syrup or lemon juice over the cooked pancakes.
- sifting some icing sugar on top.

Index

Who can help?

If you or someone you know is suffering from an eating disorder, these services can help:

Your local Doctor's Surgery will be able to provide you with advice and recommended services near you. Many Doctors' surgeries can also provide help in the form of therapy or counselling.

If you are still at school, talk to your school counsellor. Your workplace may also have a healthcare system, which can provide you with help and support.

www.b-eat.co.uk is a registered eating disorder charity. Visit their website for online support or call their helpline:
0345 634 1414 (adults)
or 0345 634 7650 (under 18s)

Samaritans provides a 24-hour confidential service for you to get things off your chest. Call 08457 90 90 90 to chat to someone.

If you are having suicidal thoughts, call the National Suicide Prevention Hotline on 800-273-TALK (8255).
In the case of emergency call 999.

About the author

I was born in 1996 and grew up in Corsham, Wiltshire with my parents and older sister. I began my own business, Nicola Davis Crafts, selling positivity-inspired art at the age of 17. At this point I was struggling with anorexia nervosa, and spent most of my time off school. In 2014, I left school and began my recovery. I was able to expand my business further and develop confidence within myself by writing this book, aimed to help others with eating disorders.

Now, I work full time from home, making and selling my work both at craft fairs and internationally online.

I often speak about my journey and teach art at outreach programmes across the country.

I also try to raise awareness of eating disorders through the media such as in newspapers, on the radio and through social media.

Follow my business here:

www.nicoladaviscrafts.weebly.com

Twitter @ Ndaviscrafts

Facebook @ Nicola Davis Crafts

...and my recovery journey here:

Facebook @My Super Sweet Recovery Cookbook

Instagram @ Supersweetrecovery